IT'S NOT *the* DIET

AND OTHER SURPRISING SECRETS *of* LONGEVITY

CHARLES R. GORDON, M.D.

Produced with the assistance of Fluency Organization, Inc. in Tyler, TX

Cover design by Inkwell Creative

www.DesignedOnPurpose.com

ISBN 978-0-615-75347-8

To my parents,
thanks for guiding the way.
And to my patients,
your wisdom fills these pages.

I'm indebted to Pastor David O. Dykes, D.Min., for his encouragement in writing this book.

I also want to thank Mac Richard and the people of Lake Hills Church in Austin for giving me a second church home.

Finally, to Kimberly, for continuing to put up with me.

Contents

Introduction   *i*

Pillar 1 – Have a Healthy Body: **1**
    Take Care of Your House
What do you think is the secret to a good, long life?   3

What one personal change could you make this month and see an immediate result?   7

What do you think of the idea of fasting?   13

What is your favorite way to exercise?   19

What qualities do you think describe a good doctor?   25

If you had a one-of-a-kind vintage car worth millions, how well would you take care of it?   29

How many hours of sleep do you need to be at your best?   35

How do you break a bad habit?   39

Pillar 2 – Focus on Blessing: **41**
    Attitude Really Is Everything
Why should you count your blessings?   43

How much good news do you hear every day on the television?   49

What is your favorite book?   55

In what ways do you guard your heart and mind 59
    against negative influences?

Pillar 3 – Love Somebody: **63**
You Were Made to Be with Others
Who are the five people that you would call when 65
    the chips are down?
With whom do you most wish to "grow old"? 69
Are you quick or slow to forgive? 75
What is the best advice you've ever received about 79
    how to live a good life?
In what ways are you deeply connected to your 85
    church family?
What do you do when you feel lonely? 89
What do you enjoy most about connecting with 95
    other Believers?

Pillar 4 – Stay Busy: **99**
The Surprising Secret to Longevity
What is the key to happiness? 101
What was the best job you ever had? 105
Why do you think it's good to work hard? 111
What is the best age to retire? 115
What activity do you love doing so much that you 121
    often lose track of time?
How is work viewed in our world today? 125
What stresses you out about work? 129
What 24-hour period do you consistently set aside 135
    to rest and regroup each week?

How would you describe a workaholic?   141

What does it mean to live to God's glory?   145

A Firm Foundation – Connecting with God   **149**

Imagine living a vigorous ten decades. What   151
    would life be like?

What activity, work or service makes you feel   157
    useful?

Is it possible to die before your time?   163

What one sentence do you want inscribed on your   169
    tombstone?

Are you afraid of dying?   175

Putting It All Together   **179**

Endnotes   **185**

With long life will I

SATISFY HIM

and show him my

SALVATION.

-Psalm 91:16

INTRODUCTION

Building Your House of Longevity

Carol Foley is a very persistent person. If she really wants something, she is not the kind who gives up easily. Willard Scott, on the *Today Show*, knows this because she called his staff nearly every day for a year. Her daily calls were on behalf of her spunky grandmother, Mygnone Boone (Nonnie for short) who was about to celebrate her one-hundredth birthday. Nonnie was born in what seems another era. She had lived to see the first cars on the road, remembered seeing the telephone installed and raised a family in a quieter time before cell phones and computers came to rule our lives.

This is not to say that her life was easy. She survived the Great Depression and two world wars. She outlived a husband and four siblings. Still, she remained sharp and active, found joy and laughter in every day—and she was about to turn 100 years old! But despite her amazing accomplishments, and Carol's determination, Willard Scott never got around to mentioning her on the birthdays/anniversaries segment of the *Today Show*. Why? *There are simply too many people turning one hundred to mention them all*. In fact, never in recent history has there been such an overabundance of centenarians. Why is this? What are their secrets? And more to the point: are you ready to join them?

Happily, this is not a book about a new diet or exercise regime. And though I am a medical doctor and wholeheartedly applaud good medical care, this isn't a book offering medical advice—at least not the usual kind.

Simply stated, this is a book about the amazing observations I've learned from listening to my patients. Namely, that the surest way to live to be 101 is to follow biblical principles. And perhaps not surprisingly, these secrets don't get much coverage in our popular press. But the Bible has more to say about living a long, full life than most people recognize. And like gems hidden in plain sight, I have learned 4 simple principles that can and will add years to your life.

I'm not just talking about living to be older—I'm talking about living *well*. This, in fact, is what we are designed to do. And modern medicine is making it more likely that many of us will live much longer than we ever thought possible.

- The older population in 2030 is projected to be twice as large as in 2000, growing from 35 million to 72 million and representing nearly 20% of the total U.S. population.[1]
- The U.S. Census Bureau projects that the population age 85 and over could grow from 5.5 million in 2010 to 19 million by 2050.[2]

The thing is, few of us take time to prepare for this amazing future. Yes, *you* will probably live to be older than you expect. But the great news is that you don't have to dread it! What I have learned in my medical practice is that our later years can be—and should be—full of joy, purpose and meaning.

When I am privileged to care for patients who have lived over eight or nine decades on this planet, I ask: "What's your secret?" Invariably, the responses range from the serious to the funny. I've heard everything from, "Drink two glasses of wine at night, but you never finish the second one," to "You have to work like a mule!" However, what I've noticed is that there are a few common threads. One thing I have never heard is that you have to protect your telomeres. But, in fact, these long-lived patients do just that.

The telomeres are the end strands of your DNA. Researchers have found that the telomeres get shorter and shorter with age, due to disease and the ravages of time. The telomeres eventually get so short that we cannot make proteins very well anymore, so we begin aging and we eventually die.

Are there any other animals that do a better job of protecting their telomeres than we do? The answer is absolutely "yes." In fact, the bowhead whale, probably the longest living mammal, frequently lives up to 200 years. In studying these mammals, scientists have found old spearheads from the early 1800s lodged inside! In other words, some of these giant sea creatures evaded the whaler's harpoon and outlived their great- great-grandchildren.

The bowhead whale, however, is not the longest-living *animal*. One contender for that distinction is the Galapagos tortoise. If not killed by a predator or human, they can live 250 years or more. Don't you wish they could talk? Some of these guys were around before George Washington was elected President.

However, the tortoise is a short-timer compared to the longest living animal on earth. It is actually one of my favorites: the brain coral—so named because it bears a striking resemblance to the human brain. It really is an animal, part of the Faviidae scientific family, and it can live over 500 years. If you happen to be snorkeling and see one of these, what you are looking at may have been around when Shakespeare was penning *Hamlet*.

As amazing as our friend the brain coral is, it is a lightweight in comparison to the longest living organism. The U.S. Forest Service has identified a unique grove of trees in California. Among this group of Bristle Cone pine trees stands one gnarled piece of living history aptly named Methuselah. Of course, the oldest man ever was the original Methuselah, who lived to the ripe old age of 969, according to Genesis 5:27. This tree has him beat. Scientists have studied the rings of the Methuselah pine and know that it is over 4,700 years old. No kidding—this tree was 3,000 years old when Jesus was born! Sadly, the Parks and Wildlife Department has to keep Methuselah's location secret for fear of arson…but that's another story.

The point is that we, as part of God's creation, can do a much better job of taking care of our bodies (including our telomeres) and enjoy a much longer and healthier life. Researchers have identified different parts of the world where people live remarkably longer than other human beings. For example, the world's longest-lived women are found on the island of Okinawa, while a Mediterranean island near Italy has the highest concentration of male centenarians.[3] The island of Ikarian off the coast of Turkey has drawn researchers because of how many healthy, robust people over 80 and 90 years old reside there.[4]

What is their secret? Well, it turns out it's not just one thing in particular. Rather, it is a bunch of small things that add up. Call it the centenarian lifestyle. And here is the surprising part: few of these folks pay a lot of attention to what they eat. Nor do they follow a challenging fitness routine. Furthermore, these people are not living on autopilot with nothing to do—far from it! In fact, these people are some of the most vigorous you'll find. In the remaining pages of this book, we'll seek to uncover the secrets to their surprising success.

I think our secular society has it all wrong when it comes to living well and living a long time. A good illustration is what I like to call, the "Tale of the Two Billy's." The other day, I heard Billy Joel's catchy song called, "Only the Good Die Young." I sang along to every word.

But just because something's catchy doesn't mean it's good theology. As a rule, the good die old.

There is another Billy—the evangelist, Billy Graham, who at this writing is 94 years young. He is a much more realistic example of what happens to good people. As a neurosurgeon, I have to deal with death and dying. What I've found is that Billy Joel should have sung something like, "It really only bothers us when the good die young." When an elderly saint has gone on to heaven, we're not terribly broken up over it. It's time. Or if someone has been drinking and taking drugs and gets involved in an automobile accident, we often think, "Well, he had it coming to him." It really only bothers us when the good die young. What I want to suggest is that innocent, good people who die young are actually rare, and that is why their stories make the news.

There is a National Institute of Health study by Dr. Michael McCullough called a metanalysis (a study of studies).[5] On your tax dime, researchers did a statistical analysis of previous studies on aging and longevity. They compiled the traits of all the longest-living people across 47 high-caliber studies. One of the things they discovered is that regular religious involvement confers about an extra decade to a person's life.[6] Taking it a step further, I consider a personal relationship with God (not just religious involvement) to be the foundation to a person's longevity.

This study got me thinking about how living a good, long life is like building a house—a house of longevity. It takes a good plan and hard work to build a house—the same is true if we want to live to be 101. If a relationship with God is the foundation, then what are the pillars supporting this "house"? What I've learned in listening to my patients is that there are 4 basic principles that they all articulate to some degree. Not surprisingly, these principles (or pillars) are found in the pages of the Bible. If we strive to live to be 101 (and we should), we ought to be busy working on these 4 pillars throughout our lives. This book is divided into sections to coincide with these 4 pillars:

Section One
Pillar 1 - Have a Healthy Body: Take Care of Your House

Section Two
Pillar 2 - Focus on Blessing: Attitude Really Is Everything

Section Three
Pillar 3 - Love Somebody: You Are Made to Be with Others

Section Four
Pillar 4 - Stay Busy: The Surprising Secret to Longevity

It's Not the Diet

Section Five is about establishing a firm foundation for our lives—connecting with God and nurturing our relationship with our heavenly Father.

As I've listened to my patients who have lived long, full lives, I've also found that many of them are hilarious people. Maybe it's because they just don't care what people think. Or, maybe having a good sense of humor actually helps you to live longer.

Anyway, I've included some of their anecdotes. They have a lot to teach us. Again, I'm not talking about living in a vegetative state at 101 years of age. No one wants to live to be 101 if that's what life is going to be like. I mean reaching our full potential with our minds and our health intact until it's time for us to go home. The Bible refers to this as a "ripe old age" like "sheaves gathered in season" (Job 5:26).

And there, my friend, is your calling.

Pillar 1

Have a Healthy Body: Take Care of Your House

"I can't afford to die. It'll wreck my image."[7]

Jack LaLanne, exercise guru, lived to 96

WHat do you think is the secret to a good, long life?

Several years ago, we wanted to put our house up for sale, so we enlisted the aid of a realtor. After she walked through the house, she advised us to make some changes before listing. First, she said to clean the carpets. Really clean them. (We have four children, mind you.) She also suggested putting a new coat of paint in the kitchen and doing a couple of minor repairs. It was amazing. The place looked new again. How had we lived there before? A few, simple changes made an incredible difference.

I have a question for you. What changes do you need to make to your house? I don't mean the physical street address where you live. I mean the body in which your soul lives. The idea of your body as a dwelling is not original with me. The Bible compares the body to a temple—a dwelling place for God Himself. Paul tells us that our body is the home of the Holy Spirit (1 Corinthians 6:19-20).

As we found with our home, it doesn't necessarily have to be extraordinary changes that make a difference. In fact, if you live in America, your odds of living to be 101 are already better than most.

If you want to have your "house" in tip-top shape, I submit that there are three simple steps to take. And the great news is that you can start these steps today!

You know you're
getting old when
THE CANDLES
cost more than
THE CAKE.

-Bob Hope, comedian,
lived to 100

WHAT ONE PERSONAL CHANGE COULD YOU MAKE THIS MONTH AND SEE AN IMMEDIATE RESULT?

Step One in getting your house in order is to learn to stop. Stop eating when you are full. I promised this isn't your ordinary diet and exercise book. And I have some really fabulous news: you don't have to lose weight! Really! Eat what you want. In his book, *20,000 Days and Counting*, my friend Robert D. Smith goes one step further: eat dessert first![8] (My wife still doesn't buy that one, but I'm working on her.)

I had a chance one time to visit with Lou Holtz, the former coach of Notre Dame who now serves as an ESPN commentator. At age 76, he is still so sharp and fit, it's inspiring. So, of course, I had to ask when I met him: "What's your secret? How do you stay in such great shape?" Knowing I'm a doctor, he hesitated with his answer. "I hate to tell you, Doc…" he began and then proceeded to tell me that he "doesn't diet." "I eat anything I want, anytime I want," he explained. Then he added: "But I never eat unless I'm hungry." And there you have it: the Lou Diet.

But let me caution you—it's not as easy as it sounds. You have to be disciplined. Gluttony is a sin, according to the Bible. Gluttony is when we stop eating for nutrition and start trying to fill some need within us that has nothing to do with our stomachs. For me, stress eating is the problem. There really is such a thing as comfort food and, for me, it is chocolate. Something troubling you? Have a snack. Stressed? Have a bite!

Even still, the latest medical studies have made us completely re-think our definition of healthy weight. In evaluating almost 100 previous studies involving three million people, researchers concluded that being overweight or slightly obese was linked to about a 6% lower risk of dying, compared to people considered "normal weight."[9]

The short version is this: no, you don't want to be fat. But neither do you want to be model-skinny—praise the Lord! Really and truly, the people who live the longest are "Goldilocks weight"—just right. Scientists talk about the importance of a healthy BMI (Body Mass Index, or the relation of your height to your weight). Surprisingly, it turns out that what we used to consider "mildly overweight" (about 15 pounds) is just perfect!

It's funny—in the 1800s, a "15-pounds over" weight class was considered ideal. But we've consistently lowered our goals of "ideal" body weight over the years. Maybe our 19th Century predecessors weren't so far off after all—and that's great news for most of us!

A man 90 years old was asked to what he attributed his LONGEVITY.

"I reckon," he said with a twinkle in his eye, "it's because most nights I went to bed and slept when I SHOULD HAVE SAT UP AND WORRIED."

-told by Garson Kanin, American playright, lived to 87

WHAT DO YOU THINK OF THE IDEA OF FASTING?

Picture in your mind's eye a young man carrying something you want. You run as fast as you can, knocking him over, and forcibly take his item. This type of behavior will get you arrested, unless you are a defensive back in a football game. Then it will get you thousands of adoring fans and a post-game interview. Or, let's say you sell thousands of nearly worthless tickets to unsuspecting dupes. This will land you in court, unless you are on Wall Street or selling lottery stubs. The context of what we do makes all the difference.

So too with eating. The Bible does have a lot to say about it. And it never mentions the word "carb." But what it does seem to emphasize is that we receive food as a blessing. Genesis 1:29 reminds us what we often forget: all food is from God. We are to be grateful for it.

Then, too, there is a lot of discussion about fasting and feasting. Fasting is a regular occasion, always accompanied by prayer. Feasting is part of celebration—and just as much a part of God's plan for living long and healthy lives. But both are a part of the same lifestyle. What is interesting is that, once again, medical science is confirming what Bible scholars have known for centuries. Numerous studies suggest that our bodies function better when we have times of both feasting and fasting.[10] Perhaps our hunter-gatherer ancestors experienced the same pattern, and our metabolism responds to it.

Always, God's primary interest is in our worship, not our metabolism. And it boils down to *context*. When we feast (and when we fast) it is for a higher purpose.

> "So whether you eat or drink or whatever you do, do it all for the glory of God."
>
> 1 CORINTHIANS 10:31

The secret to

LONGEVITY

is to keep

BREATHING.

-Sophie Tucker,
entertainer (1886-1996)

What *is* your favorite way to exercise?

S tep Two in updating your "house" is to take a couple more steps. Here's the deal—there's a huge (and I mean gigantic) fitness industry out there. Next to endless diets (most of which don't work), the most popular advice given by the press is that we need to exercise more. And I think it's bogus.

We never read of Jesus hitting the gym! What we do know is that He walked. And walked. Everybody in Bible times walked just about everywhere they went. Walking is the most underappreciated exercise in Western culture. You were made to walk. And if you walk a little over a mile a day, it's likely that you will live longer than couch potatoes.[11] This is probably why city folk are experiencing less obesity than their rural counterparts: they just walk more![12]

Walking has other fabulous health benefits. It clears your mind, and if you walk with a friend, you get double duty benefits (more on that later). It's good for your joints; it can reduce cholesterol and lower your blood pressure; plus, it can improve your mood.

But I know what you are thinking: *When can I find the time?* This, in fact, is a big challenge, isn't it? Walking doesn't pay well, monetarily speaking, and we tend to value *only* those things that are compensated. Where am I going here? I'm going back where I started—to the story of getting our house ready to sell.

The realtor did not advise us to reroof our house, install new flooring or make some other drastic change in order to attract more buyers. The changes she suggested were minor and very doable—and guess what?We made her changes and we sold our house.

This is what is so great about walking a little every day. You really can do it! Fifteen to twenty minutes is all it takes. You just need to decide to do it. Here's a hint: trade time watching TV for time walking. Congratulations! You just added another decade to your life!

How do you live a long life?

Take a two-mile walk

every morning

Before Breakfast.

-President Harry S. Truman,
lived to 88

WHAT QUALITIES DO YOU THINK DESCRIBE A GOOD DOCTOR?

Step Three is to listen to your doctor. This statement is usually listed in diet and exercise books as a disclaimer. "Don't mistake this crazy health plan as real medical advice," they say. But I mean this as sincere counsel. I have a doctor, and I wouldn't trade him for all the tea in China!

There are a few medically proven health measures that can literally add years to your life. Many studies recommend taking a baby aspirin every day. But this doesn't apply to everybody—some people with a history of bleeding ulcers should avoid aspirin like the plague! There are dozens of similar examples. Your doctor will take a medical history and give you advice. It is up to *you* to follow his or her directions.

Find a physician who looks you in the eye and tells you the truth. The medical profession is under siege today—that's a topic for another book. But what hasn't changed is this: there is no substitute for a primary care doctor who knows you and your medical history. He or she can help you stop smoking, tell you when to get a colonoscopy, let you know if that mole needs to be removed—and be entrusted with your deepest secrets.

You literally can't put a price on the value of a caring, qualified family physician. They are the gems of our medical system. Find someone you trust and stick with him or her like glue! Do what they say—and you can thank me later!

I have a

TWO-STORY HOUSE

and

a very bad

memory.

-*Betty White, actress, 91
on her secret to staying fit*[13]

IF YOU HAD A ONE-OF-A-KIND VINTAGE CAR WORTH MILLIONS, HOW WELL WOULD YOU TAKE CARE OF IT?

P icture in your mind's eye your very favorite automobile. Ladies, this picture may not do much for you, but it gets to me right down in my soul. When I think of my favorite car, I think of a 1962 Ferrari GTO. In fact, an odd color 1962 Ferrari GTO sold in 2011 for $35,000,000, one of two pea green Ferraris ever made (and one of only 39 1962 Ferrari GTOs ever built).

The reason this car is so coveted is because this was the first time the Ferrari engineers combined forces to study every element of what makes a great car, down to the aerodynamics. The result was the 1962 Ferrari GTO, with its beautiful, sleek lines. It became the forerunner of every sports car you see on the street.

Now imagine, if you will, that you have a rich uncle who happened to pass away and bequeathed to you a 1962 Ferrari GTO. First, you'd be a millionaire several times over and you'd be ecstatic! But the next thing you would do, I suggest, is start taking excellent care of this gift. You would leave it indoors. You would have mechanics service it and you would spare no expense to preserve this gem.

What you wouldn't do is leave it to the elements to suffer from neglect like an old piece of junk. But here's the rub: that Ferrari pales in comparison to your body. Seriously.

Still, I see people who treat their Ferrari GTO bodies like the owner of a junkyard car. They go without regular checkups. They don't exercise. They don't take care of themselves. They smoke and overindulge, never see a dentist and basically abuse their bodies. Then they wonder at middle age why they start to fall apart. Take care of the machine that God gave you—and it will take care of you!

Old people

SHOULDN'T *eat*

HEALTH FOODS.

They need all the

PRESERVATIVES

they can get.

-George Burns, comedian,
lived to 100

HOW MANY HOURS OF SLEEP DO YOU NEED TO BE AT YOUR BEST?

When I was in my residency, we lived in a culture of sleep deprivation. We would compete to see who could go the longest without closing his eyes. It was both crazy and dangerous. And during this time, it came to light that patients were literally dying because resident physicians were so sleep deprived. Since then, thankfully, laws have been put in place to limit resident workweeks to no more than 80 hours.[14]

But what I learned working several days and nights straight is that as you become more fatigued, you begin to become less compassionate. And on the edge of exhaustion, you truly don't think clearly.

Which brings me to the final segment of our first pillar of our physical health—getting a good night's sleep. The science of sleep medicine has made tremendous progress over the last few decades. We understand better that as we age, our sleep patterns change, and we have better options to treat sleeping disorders than ever before.

Even still, many patients suffer from undiagnosed and untreated sleep disorders. It starts by giving yourself adequate time to unwind and fall asleep. Don't be so tempted to "burn the candle at both ends." (That candle, by the way, is your life.) And if, after arranging your schedule to allow for adequate sleep, you still struggle with it, see your doctor. You will be glad you did!

It ain't over
'TIL IT'S OVER.

-*Yogi Berra, baseball legend*
(b. 1925 - present)

How do you break a bad habit?

S moking.

Don't start. If you have started, you have to quit.

It's hard, but not as hard as it used to be. Talk to your doctor about new treatments that make it easier.

Pillar 2

Focus on Blessing: Attitude Really Is Everything

"Give thanks in all circumstances, for this is God's will for you in Christ Jesus."

1 Thessalonians 5:18

WHY SHOULD YOU COUNT YOUR BLESSINGS?

I t's been said that some people look at life like a half-filled glass of water. Some see it as "half empty" and some see it more optimistically as "half full." One thing I've noticed in my older patients is that they are "half full" people. Invariably. They aren't Pollyannas with their heads in the sand, pretending that everything is okay. They are realists, but their *focus* is on their blessings. They find the good in every situation. This is what the Bible says to do:

> "With praise and thanksgiving they
> sang to the Lord: 'He is good; his love to
> Israel endures forever.' And all the people

gave a great shout of praise to the Lord, because the foundation of the house of the Lord was laid."

EZRA 3:11

"Enter his gates with thanksgiving and his courts with praise; give thanks to him and praise his name."

PSALM 100:4

"Do not be anxious about anything, but in everything, by prayer and petition, with thanksgiving, present your requests to God."

PHILIPPIANS 4:6

The second pillar of longevity deals with your outlook on life. If there is one missing ingredient in our society today, it's gratitude. We live longer, healthier, richer lives than any generation before us. But that doesn't "sell." Instead, turn on any cable news channel and you'll be confronted with a barrage of fear, misery and destruction. The Bible says that the evil one has come to "steal, kill and destroy" (John 10:10) and he gets all the television coverage!

The best thing about

BE*i*NG 100

is that there's

NO PE*e*R

PR*e*SS*u*R*e*.

-*Anonymous*

How much good news do you hear every day on the television?

James Keown seemed to have it all. He had a beautiful wife, a promising career and a bright future. However, when his wife Julie was admitted to the hospital with slurred speech and confusion in August of 2004, it was clear that something was terribly wrong. After Julie died a few weeks later, an autopsy determined that she had been slowly poisoned to death with antifreeze. James was later convicted of murder when police discovered he had been pouring antifreeze into his wife's Gatorade drink. Little by little, without even knowing it, she was being poisoned. Horrifying. Who would do such a thing?

Well—we are. As a society, we are poisoning our minds. And at the top of the list of mind poisons is your favorite cable news show. It is impossible to consume a steady diet of 24-hour cable news and have an attitude of thankfulness. And don't even try to tell me that you need to "stay informed." Cable news doesn't inform—it sells. And what it sells is fear, ever so slowly poisoning your mind.

Studies have shown that every 30 minutes spent in front of the television has the same life-shortening threat as smoking two cigarettes.[15] They also concluded that every hour spent watching television erases 21.8 minutes from one's life expectancy.[16] Many years ago, my wife and I attended a seminar by Bible teacher Bill Gothard. I remember he shared Psalm 1:1, which reads: "Blessed is the man who does not sit in the seat of scoffers." I wasn't sure what sitting in a seat of a scoffer was—until he displayed a picture of a man sitting on a couch in front of a television. I never forgot that mental image. Now, I can't shake that image every time I sit on the couch and grab the remote—unless ESPN is on.

So, arise from your recliner! Hide the remote! Renounce the scoffers!

We would worry less if we PRAISED MORE. Thanksgiving is the enemy of DISCONTENT AND DISSATISFACTION.

-Harry A. Ironside, pastor
(1876-1951)

What *is* your favorite book?

There is a rare books and manuscripts library at Yale University in New Haven, Connecticut, that contains some of the most valuable texts in the entire world. Many are one-of-a-kind, including a copy of one of the few remaining original Gutenberg Bibles. We value these books so much that they've been encased in hermetically sealed environments, protected from light and maintained at constant humidity levels.

We know that physical exercise is a key factor to one's health, but so is mental exercise. A number of senior adults I talked to while researching for this book told me they enjoy reading as a daily exercise for their brain. One lady who is 84 years old said she had read thousands of books since her husband died. Doing crossword puzzles, playing challenging games online or with others—these types of activities will help you stay mentally sharp.[17]

Perhaps the most useful skill to learn is to take up another language. Numerous studies have documented that people who are bilingual think faster and have a lower incidence of dementia.[18] The point is: you have to stretch your brain. Find a daily mental challenge that is taxing. Mental exercise is similar to going to the gym—if it's too easy, it doesn't help!

And in the end,
it's not the years
in your life

that count.

It's the life in

your years.

-*President Abraham Lincoln*

In what ways do you guard your heart and mind against negative influences?

The secret to longevity is firmly rooted in being happy and healthy. But it's not just what you eat and what you breathe that's important; it's what you see and hear. This is where the Ten Commandments come into place.

The first commandment God ever gave us that came with a promise is, "Honor your father and mother so that you may live long in the land the LORD your God is giving you," Exodus 20:12. Here, God makes the connection between honoring the principles our parents taught us and living a long life as a result.

Whatever you're putting before your eyes (in terms of what you read, the television shows and movies you choose to watch, the websites you visit) is important. Whatever you're engaged in, whatever you're listening to, whatever entertains you, I have one question to ask you: Would your momma be okay with that? To me, that's the only litmus test you need!

The Bible says that if you honor your father and mother, you're going to live a longer life. On the other hand, the Bible very clearly ties together a person's poor decisions and shortening his/her life as a result.

"…bloodthirsty and deceitful men
will not live out half their days."
PSALM 55:23

Pause with me here. I've always stumbled over the "bloodthirsty" adjective. It's so descriptive. But when you look at the deeper meaning, it becomes clear. It's as if the Psalmist clears his throat and says, "Get this: your choices, your attitudes—they are *everything*. They quite literally can mean the difference in life and death."

It's simple cause and effect. We can lengthen or shorten our lives by the good and bad choices we make.

Pillar 3

Love Somebody: You Were Made to Be with Others

"If you live to be a hundred, I want to live to be a hundred minus one day so I never have to live without you."

Winnie the Pooh[19]

WHO ARE THE FIVE PEOPLE THAT YOU WOULD CALL WHEN THE CHIPS ARE DOWN?

I don't see any 95-year-olds who come to me by themselves. In fact, if you're 95 and you come to see me, I know two things about you for sure. Number one, I know that somebody loves you and cares enough about you that they've taken time out of their schedule to take you to the doctor. In other words, you didn't get there by yourself! Second, I know that you are a person who cares deeply about others and are actively engaged in other people's lives. That's why others love you and are willing to help take care of you.

The connection between loving others and longevity comes straight out of Ecclesiastes:

> "…a cord of three strands is not easily broken,"
> *ECCLESIASTES 4:12.*

Study after study has shown that the people who are engaged with a loving family, whether it's a church family, a community or a collection of close-knit relatives, live longer. I'm talking decades longer! I cannot overemphasize the importance of family and friends.

I wouldn't have
made it this far
without the
LOVE OF MY
WIFE OF 67
YEARS.
She's stood by me all
this time and told
me I'm a good man.
MOST DAYS.

-Vinnie, 87

WITH WHOM DO YOU MOST WISH TO "GROW OLD"?

My wife's grandmother had a simple, country home. There were quilts everywhere and the smell of something good wafting from the kitchen. On the wall, she had a framed piece of embroidery with the words: "A nagging wife may save your life!"

So true. We need each other. Especially men—we need our wives. Did you know that if a husband dies, the surviving spouse has no increased risk of mortality the following year? This was discovered by a scientific study of married people born between 1910 and 1930.[20] However, they found that if the wife dies, the husband was 30% more likely to die. Why is this? Clearly, it's true: men really cannot take care of themselves!

Honestly, I am the recipient of my wife's watchful eye. Before we were even married, she found a malignant melanoma hidden on my scalp. "You better get that checked," she warned.

"Just a birthmark," I retorted.

Then the bearer-of-truth spoke up, "That's no birthmark. Go get it checked!"

Sure enough, she was right and her advice saved my life. The Bible says, "Houses and wealth are inherited from parents, but a prudent wife is from the Lord," Proverbs 19:14. We really do need each other to make it every day. Remember what the Bible says about a cord of three strands? "Though one may be overpowered, two can defend themselves.

A cord of three strands is not quickly broken," Ecclesiastes 4:12. Clearly, the Bible teaches that we are created for relationships. We are meant to live with others. In my entire medical practice, I've never met a 101-year-old hermit!

Bear with each other and

FORGIVE

whatever grievances you

may have against

one another.

FORGIVE AS THE

LORD FORGAVE YOU.

Colossians 3:13

Are you quick or slow to forgive?

Forgive quickly.

None of my 90-year-old patients waste much time carrying a grudge. One of my older patients told me it "got too heavy" after a while.

Anyone can get old.

All you have to do is

LIVE LONG

ENOUGH.

-Groucho Marx,
comedian, lived to 87

WHAT *is* THE BEST ADVICE *YOU*'VE EVER RECEIVED *ABOUT* HOW TO LIVE *A* GOOD LIFE?

I like to go running in Faulkner Park near my home in Tyler. Oftentimes, I can run for several miles and not see a single person, just the animals and me. About a month ago, I encountered a couple of ladies who were sprinting at me like Olympic runners. "Hey mister," they said as they caught their breath, "there's a snake around the bend!" And they held up their hands in the East Texas yardstick, indicating a very big snake indeed! I was in lightweight shoes that are really closer to just moccasins, all alone, and my only weapon of defense was my iPhone.

I decided to man-up and keep running, but for the rest of my run I kept my eyes peeled. My heart rate was up and I was on the lookout the entire time for a venomous viper, although I never saw anything.

Initially, I was irritated that they "ruined" my run. Until I realized they really did me a favor. If I had been in their place, I would have warned them of potential danger ahead, too. In our society, we don't really appreciate prophets of doom about what's ahead if we don't change our ways. However, that's what God's Word does for us. In Ecclesiastes, it's as if Solomon comes around the bend in the road to warn us of some pitfalls ahead. We can take heed and be diligent and on the alert—or we can ignore wisdom and suffer the consequences. That's the basic difference between dying before your time and living to be a ripe old age. Let the kind of people into your life who care about you, even though you may not always like what they have to say. Listen and learn from others' advice because you might thank them one day for helping you live a longer, healthier, more productive life.

Every day, I decide, "WHAT *is* MY DAY GOING TO BE LIKE?" My day goes a little better when I decide I WILL BE WITH SOMEBODY THAT DAY.

Alice, 87

IN WHAT WAYS ARE YOU DEEPLY CONNECTED TO YOUR CHURCH FAMILY?

There is more to personal connection than just being with blood relatives. As I mentioned in the introduction, one of the common themes of Dr. McCullough's research on the studies about longevity has to do with being involved in a religious community. According to his report, regular religious involvement led to an extra decade, on average, added to a person's life.[21]

That doesn't mean just watching a sermon on television once in a while, saying a little prayer, being a good person or reading a

Bible verse occasionally. It means being an integral part of a Christian community. You have to be plugged in so that you are involved and engaged in the Body of Christ—serving others and connecting with them. Go on mission trips. Volunteer with children. Help teenagers. Join a small group to study the Bible and pray together. Make a difference.

As one senior adult told me, at retirement it's easy to lose a lot of your relationships because you're no longer going into the office or doing your normal routines. No matter what our age, it's important to intentionally find a meaningful use of our time that also includes people.

If you do that, you can expect that this kind of active connection with others, especially those in the church community, can add at least a decade to your life.

One of the things I enjoy about being with people my own age is that THEY DON'T MIND THAT I'M OLD. THEY UNDERSTAND!

-Betty, 86

What do you do when you feel lonely?

It starts when we are born and never goes away. Our need for human touch. A study of orphans from WWII showed a marked decrease in an infant's ability to thrive when only fed and changed without the benefit of human touch. Other more recent studies have confirmed the need to routinely touch and lightly massage premature babies, which is believed to release certain chemicals in the brain.[22]

But it doesn't stop there. God was so concerned that we stay connected to other people throughout our lives that He gave us a warning sign to let us know when we need fellowship. That warning sign is called loneliness. If you get a fever, you know it's time to seek medical treatment. If you are feeling lonely, it's time to get out and go help others—for there is no more certain antidote to depression than that of service. And the perfect place to start is in church.

In fact, there is a correlation between feeling lonely and having poor health. The Bible points out the relationship between losing hope and losing one's health. "Hope deferred makes the heart sick…" Proverbs 13:12. As we grow old, it's more important than ever to intentionally seek and create new relationships. And, as one man in his eighties told me, it's just as important to maintain the old friendships, too. One senior adult woman I know has traveled to a reunion weekend with her high school girlfriends every year since graduation!

And we find this in God's Word: "Let us not give up meeting together, as some are in the habit of doing, but let us encourage one another…" Hebrews 10:25. Here's the point: our electronically connected society is no substitute for real relationships. You cannot have 1,000 "friends." The paralytic mentioned in Luke 5 needed only four friends to carry his cot. I like what my friend Tim Kimmel says about his friends. He says he is grooming his future pallbearers!

But really, our lives only have space for a handful of close friends. Choose them with care, and be the friend you wish them to be. You need a handful of people you can call in the middle of the night—and ones you know can call on you, too!

THE QUALITY,

not the longevity,

of one's life

is WHAT *is*

*i*MPORTANT.

-Martin Luther King, Jr.,
civil rights leader

What do you enjoy most about connecting with other Believers?

In various studies over the years, researchers have measured what is termed "social integration" as a factor in longevity. They ask respondents about their marital status, friends, family size and number of people sharing their household. Many have concluded that the more connected one is to family, friends and the community, the healthier they are.

Researchers at Brigham Young University and the University of North Carolina at Chapel Hill analyzed 148 studies involving more than 300,000 men and women worldwide and found a common link: people with poor social lives averaged 50% higher odds of dying than people with greater social connections.[23] That finding is about the same as the odds between smokers and non-smokers—it's that significant. Although researchers still don't yet understand exactly why this is true, it makes sense. Those who are healthy enough to get out and about are usually, well, out and about!

Never underestimate the value of your family, friends and extended family at your church. Does it matter if you go to church? Does it matter if you are part of a small group of believers who care for one another and offer prayer and support? The Bible says so—and now we have medical science to back up what the Bible has said all along.

Pillar 4:

Stay Busy:
The Surprising Secret
to Longevity

"If you want something done, ask a busy person to do it. The more things you do, the more you *can* do."

Lucille Ball, actress

What *is* the key to happiness?

Ask anyone on your block, "What is the key to happiness?" You'll get a dozen different answers. But for millions of lottery players, the answer seems obvious: happiness is just six numbers away. But something odd seems to happen on the way to the bank. In fact, if there was anyone who experienced the "lifestyle of the rich and famous," it was King Solomon. Money: he had it. Fame: ditto. Pleasure? Are you kidding? Solomon himself said, "I denied myself nothing my eyes desired; I refused my heart no pleasure," Ecclesiastes 2:10.

He had dozens of wives and thousands of concubines—and he was attended to by countless slaves. Sounds exhausting, right?

It was. Like everything else he tried to make himself happy, this too was " all vanity…" (2:11).

What about wisdom? There's a virtue. We value information in our society today. We put Nobel laureates on a pedestal, and we listen to what they have to say. Solomon was the wisest man to ever live. Surely all of his wisdom, knowledge and learning would satisfy. Nope. Solomon warned, "This too was meaningless…" (2:15).

There is something even greater than wisdom that ultimately leads to greater happiness throughout our lives. There was only one thing on earth (or "under the sun," as he put it) that satisfied him. And that leads me to the surprising secret of living well: learning to enjoy your work!

So I saw that there is

NOTHiNG

BeTTeR

for a man than to

eNJOY HiS

WORK...

Ecclesiastes 3:22

What was the best job you ever had?

Work doesn't get much positive press these days, does it? At least not until you are out of a job. And even then, it seems that we view work as a necessary evil. Ever notice how work is compared to prison, except prison has better benefits?

We strive for the day that we don't have to work anymore. An entire industry has sprung up around helping us save for retirement. And then another huge business has devoted itself to helping us spend that same retirement! I find it interesting, then, that throughout its pages, the Bible commands us to work:

"May the favor of the Lord our God rest on us; establish the work of our hands for us…"

PSALM 90:17

"You will eat the fruit of your labor; blessings and prosperity will be yours."

PSALM 128:2

"Those who work their land will have abundant food, but those who chase fantasies have no sense."

PROVERBS 12:11

"…every man should eat and drink, and enjoy the good of all his labor, it is the gift of God."

ECCLESIASTES 3:13

"I have brought you glory on earth by completing the work you gave me to do."

JOHN 17:4

The importance of work is backed up by numerous medical studies as well. A famous study of Shell Oil employees found that those who retired at age 55 and lived to be 65 had an 89% greater chance of dying in those 10 years than their counterparts who stayed at work until age 65.[24] And a more recent European study shows this to be particularly true in men.[25] It turns out, many men who retire early spend their extra time drinking and smoking—no wonder!

As you can see, it is not just a good idea to work and stay busy—it is good for you. God designed it that way.

Every man desires to

LiVe LONG,

but no man wishes

TO BE OLD.

-*Jonathan Swift, essayist,*
(1667-1745)

WHY DO YOU THINK IT'S GOOD TO WORK HARD?

A few years ago, Drs. Howard Friedman and Leslie Martin wrote a book called *The Longevity Project*.[26] They completed a study begun in 1921 by a brilliant researcher at Stanford University who studied 1,500 children ages 10 to 12 years old. A ten-year-old in 1921 would be nearly 100 years old today. What they discovered about the connection between work and longevity is fascinating.

Drs. Friedman and Martin followed this same group of 1,500 kids through their adult life into middle and old age. They tried to understand the common threads in the lives of these kids who outlived their peers. Many of their conclusions were surprising. For example, they found that people do not die from the stress of working long hours at a challenging job. In fact, the ones who worked the hardest lived the longest!

Believe it or not, these researchers discovered a truth straight out of Ecclesiastes. "A man can do nothing better than to eat and drink and find satisfaction in his work," Ecclesiastes 2:24. In other words, there is nothing better for someone to do than to be busy enjoying his or her work. When people stop working, they start dying.

OPPORTUNITY

is missed by most

people because it is

dressed in overalls and

LOOKS LIKE

WORK.

-Thomas Edison, inventor,
lived to 84

What is the best age to retire?

I think some of the popular disdain that our culture heaps on "work" is because we invariably associate work with a paycheck. We also associate it with drudgery and grumpy bosses (think *Dilbert* or *The Office*). We consider "work" and "employment" synonyms, but that's not at all what the Bible talks about. Anyone who has ever raised children, volunteered, been on a mission trip or who has taught Sunday school knows that you don't have to get paid to do work.

Here's the difference: Solomon said that people need to *enjoy* their work. In his groundbreaking book called *So Good They Can't Ignore You*, author Cal Newport points out that people who enjoy their work develop what he calls "rare and valuable skills" and pursue a "craftsman's mentality" in the pursuit of service.[27] Ahh. There it is— the s-word. Service.

I think what causes so much of our trouble is that we often forget the person for whom we work. Hint: it's *not* your boss!

> "Whatever you do, work at it with all your heart, as working for the Lord, not for men…"
> COLOSSIANS 3:23

The idea of "retirement" is a relatively modern one. It doesn't originate with the Bible. Some have traced the official idea of retiring to a German chancellor in the 1800s who offered a pension to those age 65 and over.[28]

And there's nothing wrong with retiring, per se. However, you just can't "drop out." You have to stay busy, fully engaged in service, problem solving and life in order to receive the blessings in store.

Many of the seniors I talked to were busy volunteering at their church and within their community. I know of one man who is in his nineties and still serves as superintendent of schools, traveling hundreds of miles every year. Another senior I know who is in his nineties volunteers every week at his church to help with odd jobs like folding worship bulletins and getting materials ready for the weekend services. Another lady is over 100 years old and still serves as a "Pink Lady" community volunteer in a local hospital where I live. She's there every day, making a difference.

So if you get to the point in life that you don't have to work for employment anymore, praise God! But you need to find something else to do besides sit around and control the television remote, or else I won't see you in my office at 85. That's just the truth.

Do you see a man SKILLED IN HIS WORK? He will serve before KINGS; he will not serve before obscure men.

Proverbs 22:29

WHAT ACTIVITY DO YOU LOVE DOING SO MUCH THAT YOU OFTEN LOSE TRACK OF TIME?

The Bible gives us several reasons why work is a blessing. In the opening chapter as the curtain rises on Genesis, we see God is working, creating the world. He's building for the first six days of Creation. Before the Fall where Adam sinned, God commanded that Adam work in the garden He created. Even before sin came into the world, Adam was working.

In fact, Jesus says in John 5:17, "My Father is at work even now and so, too, I am working." Someone has pointed out that God could have made a big cruise ship and just headed out to sea instead of creating the Universe, but He chose to work and create. So we are made in His image and are called to do the same.

The next reason we know work is a blessing is because God commands it. In the beginning, God put Adam to work in the Garden of Eden. "The Lord God took the man and put him in the Garden of Eden *to work it* and take care of it," Genesis 2:15.

Unambiguously, we need to work. Paul writes, "He who has been stealing must steal no longer, *but must work*, doing something useful with his own hands, that he may have something to share with those in need," Ephesians 4:28. Strong words—and a strong admonition to stay busy, if we want to live to be 101.

Anyone who stops

LEARNING

is old, whether at

TWENTY OR

EIGHTY.

-Henry Ford, American
industrialist, lived to 84

How *is* work v*i*ewe*d* *i*n *ou*r world today?

If work is so great and helps you live longer and feel better, then why is it such a drag sometimes? Why doesn't everybody just love getting up and going to work? The Bible never says that work is fun, and we all know from personal experience that work can be stressful. It can be full of drudgery, difficult bosses and tiring travel punctuated by long stretches of boredom. But being a little bored with your work simply means you have developed a level of competence. Unless there is some routine to the work you do, you haven't quite got it down.

One of my axioms of travel is, "I never want to fly with a pilot who is super excited about the takeoff." Right? Any pilot who says, "Wow! I can't wait to try a takeoff for the second time," is not my guy. Personally, I don't recommend surgeries for patients unless I know I can sleep like a baby the night before because the procedure is so routine to me. By definition, if you get really good at something it becomes very routine, mundane and even monotonous. But that is a good thing.

So here we must revisit our third pillar: gratitude. If you are so good, so accomplished, so proficient at your job that it is mundane, then you have a rare opportunity. You can be grateful that you've been entrusted with the gift of skillful service and be thankful for it.

Inaction

breeds doubt and fear. Action breeds confidence and courage. If you want to conquer fear, do not sit home and think about it.

Go out and get busy.

- Dale Carnegie, writer

What stresses you out about work?

Some people imagine that brain surgery might be stressful. No doubt, operating on the human nervous system is the most technically demanding, most stressful surgery there is. At once beautiful and terrifying, the hours creep by as your focus is confined to a small field where millimeters can literally mean the difference between life and death.

But that's not the most stressful job I've ever done. Occasionally, my wife leaves me in charge of the kids. Especially when they were little, corralling and caring for several children made brain surgery look like... well...child's play.

So how should we handle stress? There is something about stress that is counterintuitive. Author Mihaly Csikszentmihalyi, in his book *Flow: The Psychology of Optimal Experience*, documents that those who enjoy their work the most find it to be challenging, yet possible.[29] In other words, some stress is healthy. It's been said that the only people who don't experience stress are in the cemetery. Job 5:7 says, "Man is born to trouble, as sure as sparks fly upward." However, the key to handling stress is found in John 16:33: "I have told you these things, so that in me you may have peace. In this world you will have trouble. But take heart! I have overcome the world."

Also, there is a flip side to work, and it is almost absent in our society. And that is "rest," which brings us to our next biblical secret of longevity. We will inevitably get stressed out if we neglect rest—no matter how much we love (or hate) our work. Even God rested from His labor, according to Genesis 2:2. What makes us think we can do without it?

Remember the Sabbath day

by keeping it holy. Six days you shall labor and do all your work, but the seventh day is a Sabbath to the Lord your God. On it you shall not do any work… For in six days the Lord made the heavens and the earth, the sea, and all that is in them,

but he rested

on the seventh day. Therefore the Lord blessed the Sabbath day and made it holy.

Exodus 20:8-11

WHAT 24-HOUR PERIOD DO YOU CONSISTENTLY SET ASIDE TO REST AND REGROUP EACH WEEK?

I think there's another even more deeply spiritual reason that we have become so burned out with work: we've forgotten the fourth commandment. We often take the principle of honoring the Sabbath more like a suggestion. Have you ever gone to work on a weekend? Have you ever texted or emailed a work-related issue during church? I have. Thanks to modern communication, we have blurred the boundaries between work and rest so much that we can't really tell when we're resting and when we're working anymore.

My hat is off to Chick-fil-A and other retailers who are closed on Sundays. I think they've got it right. They shut the doors and turn the lights off. If a billion-dollar national restaurant can be closed one day a week, you and I can afford to do the same. I've not been to Jerusalem, but I understand they have special Sabbath elevators that stop on every floor from sundown on Friday until sunset on Saturday. Many observant Jews go to extremes to refrain from "work" on the Sabbath, including pushing elevator buttons, following an Old Testament law prohibiting fire (sparking a circuit, in this case).

I'm not saying we have to carry it that far, but I am suggesting that taking regular time off is absolutely scriptural and essential. Maybe we've become so burned out with work because we have forgotten how to rest. You've got to work well in order to rest well, and you've got to work well in order to rest well. It is a virtuous cycle. And one not limited to the Sabbath once a week.

You have to have "breathing time" every day. Take time to walk (remember?). Take time to be in fellowship. These daily habits will not only refresh you and make your days more enjoyable—they'll literally add years to your life.

We **could**
certainly slow
the *aging*
process down
if it had to work its way
through
Congress.

- Will Rogers, American
cowboy and entertainer

How would you describe a workaholic?

"A little sleep, a little slumber, a little folding of the hands to rest—and poverty will come on you like a bandit and scarcity like an armed man."

PROVERBS 6:10

vs.

"In vain you rise early and stay up late, toiling for food to eat—for he grants sleep to those he loves."

PSALM 127:2

So what is it? Are we supposed to sleep or not? For a long time, I wondered at the apparent contradiction of these two verses. Then it slowly dawned on me: it's a balance.

We all know workaholics who can't seem to rest and are constantly checking with the office, typing emails or making calls. Then we also know those who can't seem to get out of the bed in the morning!

When it comes to work and rest, they are really two sides of the same coin. We are admonished to do both. And ironically, you can't do one well if you don't do the other.

The Bible warns us to avoid the extremes. To work well, we must rest. But "…the sleep of the laborer is sweet," Ecclesiastes 5:12.

Life is like

RiDiNG *a* BiCYCLe.

To keep your balance,

YOU MUSt KeeP

MOViNG.

*-Albert Einstein, physicist
(1879-1955)*

What does it mean to live to God's glory?

I want to issue a challenge about staying busy, engaged and active throughout your life. If there is one verse that completely sums up what it takes to live to be 101, it's 1 Corinthians 10:31. Get a load of this—I call it Gordon's paraphrase. "Whatever you eat or drink, whatever you do—what you're eating, what you're drinking, what physical and mental condition you're in, what work you're doing—all of this stuff…Do it all for the glory of God."

In light of 1 Corinthians 10:31, is there anything you're doing that is not glorifying to God?

Is there anything you're doing that is working against your potential to live a long life?

Are there things you could start doing that would bring more glory to Him?

Whatever you decide, get busy doing it. When I started paying attention to what the eighty- and ninety-something patients were busy doing to live life in a productive way to the glory of God, I was amazed. One lady I know who died at 92 after a long, fulfilling life told someone when she was 91 years old: "You know, I just hope I don't live to be old." If you take me up on this challenge and stay busy glorifying God, you won't have time to grow old.

A Firm Foundation:

Connecting with God

"I still can enjoy God's presence every day. I can pray; I can encourage others; I can meditate on the promises God has given us in His Word, the Bible; I can thank God for His faithfulness to me over the years."

Billy Graham, evangelist, 94[30]

IMAGINE LIVING a VIGOROUS TEN DECADES. WHAT WOULD LIFE BE LIKE?

This idea of living out your full potential, even living to be 101, is not just my medical goal for you. In other words, don't take my word for it. Look at what God's Word says about His desire for you to live a long, robust life. In the Bible, longevity was often described as a result of or reward for righteous living. Old age was intended to be the norm.

As I began to study God's Word, I was surprised to see just how much God has to say about longevity in the Bible:

"Never again will there be in it
an infant who lives but a few days,
or an old man who does not live out his
years; *he who dies at a hundred will be
thought a mere youth…*"
ISAIAH 65:20

"My son, do not forget my teaching, but
keep my commands in your heart, *for
they will prolong your life many years*
and bring you prosperity."
PROVERBS 3:1-2

"The fear of the Lord is the beginning of
wisdom, and knowledge of the Holy One
is understanding. For through me *your
days will be many, and years will be added
to your life.*"
PROVERBS 9:10-11

Improvements in medical science and
preventative care are making it possible for

us to experience the long lifetime that God's Word describes. Do you *want* to live to be 101 years old? It's an important question because your chances of living longer than your parents are greater than ever before.

I think you should *plan* to live to be 101! And that is the point of this book, really. The question then becomes: "How do I live my fullest, longest life?"

Even to your old age

and gray hairs

I *am* he,

I am he who will sustain

you. I have made you

and I will carry you;

I will sustain

you and I will

rescue you.

Isaiah 46:4

WHAT ACTIVITY, WORK OR SERVICE MAKES YOU FEEL USEFUL?

There is a story in the Bible about a woman who lived to be at least 84 years old. For much of that time, she was a widow. The Bible tells us that she was only married about seven years.

Today, women often outlive their spouses and many of the seniors I talked to in writing this book were widows. How do they spend their time every day? The ones who are healthy, active and have positive outlooks on life are like Anna: they depend upon God. The Bible says of her:

"There was also a prophetess, Anna,
the daughter of Phanuel, of the tribe of
Asher. She was very old; she had lived
with her husband seven years after her
marriage, and then was a widow until she
was eighty-four. She never left the temple
but worshiped night and day, fasting and
praying."

LUKE 2:36-37

This was her work. I suppose Anna could
have become very despondent and depressed
after the untimely death of her husband.
She could have been overwhelmed trying to
think of how she would fill the hours now
that her spouse was gone. The life of a widow
has never been easy, but in ancient times it
was doubly hard. Still, Anna made a choice:
to connect with God and worship Him. And
because that was a daily habit of her life, she
was in the right place at the right time when
Jesus' parents brought Him to the Temple

when He was just a child. She was able to see Him with her own eyes and share about Him with others (2:38).

Anna is the perfect 4-Pillar model for us. We know she was taking care of her body because she was 84 "back in the day" when nobody lived that long. And what was she doing with her time? She was volunteering in the Temple, serving with others and worshipping. And she lived to see the Son of God. Amazing.

To me, old age is always

15 YEARS OLDER

THAN I AM.

-Francis Bacon, philosopher

Is *it* possible to die before your time?

The Bible seems to say so. It very clearly addresses this idea of premature death.

> "Do not be overwicked, and do not be a fool—*why die before your time?*"
> *Ecclesiastes 7:17*

Interestingly, Scripture ties together the idea of dying before your intended time with wicked or foolish choices. There are certain lifestyle decisions we need to make in order to reap the benefit of living a long life. If that is true, then the opposite is also true. We can make poor choices about our health and our overall approach to life that can actually short-circuit God's plans for our lives.

"The fear of the Lord adds length to life,
but *the years of the wicked are cut short.*"
PROVERBS 10:27

So is it only the wicked who die
young? Do these Scriptures and others
outlined in this book *guarantee* a long
life? Unfortunately, no. We can all think of
innocent lives cut short because of free will
run amok. Or lives lost to diseases that we
cannot cure. There are two things the Bible
says about these cases.

First, they are the exception—not the
rule. Remember the Tale of the Two Billy's?
It only bothers us when the good die young.
But boy, does it bother us! "It's wrong," we
argue. And when our hearts are broken,
God understands and even feels our pain
(Hebrews 4:15). We know this: all mourning
is temporary. In heaven one day, "He will
wipe every tear from their eyes. There will

be no more death or mourning or crying or pain, for the old order of things has passed away," Revelation 21:4.

Second, but for these exceptions, the Bible also teaches that the suffering of this world is nothing compared with the coming glory to be revealed in us (Romans 8:18). It's interesting that some of the best-selling books written lately have to do with individuals who have experienced heaven. People are hungry to hear about what happens when we die. But you don't have to pick up a best seller to know: it's fabulous.

"Then I saw a new heaven and a new earth, for the first heaven and the first earth had passed away, and there was no longer any sea. And I heard a loud voice from the throne saying, 'Now the dwelling of God is with men, and he will live with them. They will be his people, and God himself will be with them and be their God."' Revelation 21:1, 3

Whether you live to be 7 or 107, this physical existence is just a foretaste of what is to come. The Bible assures us, "Now we see but a poor reflection as in a mirror; then we shall see face to face. Now I know in part; then I shall know fully, even as I am fully known," 1 Corinthians 13:12.

The point is clear. Don't cut your years short by leaving God out of the equation. Honor and serve Him—and He will bless you as a result.

Faithful Forerunners

Abraham, 175 years old

Sarah, 127 years old

Isaac, 180 years old

Jacob, 147 years old

Joseph, 110 years old

Aaron, 123 years old

Moses, 120 years old

What one sentence do you want inscribed on your tombstone?

Knowing that we're all going to die one day, it becomes all the more important to realize that it matters how we live. Again, God's Word lets us in on the secret of what is required to live, really live, the way God intended.

> "Whoever of you loves life *and desires to see many good days*, keep your tongue from evil and your lips from speaking lies. Turn from evil and do good; seek peace and pursue it."
>
> *Psalm 34:12-14*

"Walk in all the way that the Lord your God has commanded you, so that you may live and prosper and *prolong your days* in the land that you will possess."
DEUTERONOMY 5:33

"He asked you for life, and you gave it to him—*length of days*, for ever and ever."
PSALM 21:4

"The fear of the Lord *adds length to life...*"
PROVERBS 10:27

"All hard work brings a profit, but mere talk leads only to poverty."
PROVERBS 14:23

"He has showed you, O man, what is good. And what does the Lord require of you? To act justly and to love mercy and to walk humbly with your God."
MICAH 6:8

When we turn to God as the source of our life, that's when we really begin to live.

We are basically made to give.

If we don't give, then we grow inwardly and that leads to remorse and selfishness. We can give more things than money… we can give OUR TIME, OUR BLESSINGS, OUR HUGS AND ENCOURAGEMENT.

Brian, 80

Are you afraid of dying?

I have a colleague and friend who is an oncologist, Dr. Sasha Vukelja. She says that when her patients get diagnosed with cancer, one of the first questions they ask is, "Am I going to die?"

Her answer is direct, but it's filled with a strong dose of truth. She tells them, "If you're looking to live forever, you're in the wrong clinic. We're all going to die." Her job, she explains, is to help patients not die before their time. God says in His Word that dying is part of living. We're not promised to live forever—we aren't supposed to. The Bible says in Genesis 6:3, "Then the Lord said, 'My Spirit will not contend with man forever, for he is mortal...'" God has so much more in store for you than just this brief, physical existence.

> "Jesus [said], 'I am the resurrection and the life. He who believes in me will live, even though he dies...'"
> JOHN 11:25

> "Listen, I tell you a mystery: We will not all sleep, but we will all be changed—in a flash, in the twinkling of an eye, at the last trumpet. For the trumpet will sound, the dead will be raised imperishable, and we will be changed. For the perishable must clothe itself with the imperishable, and the mortal with immortality. When the perishable has been clothed with the imperishable, and the mortal with immortality, then the saying that is written will come true: 'Death has been swallowed up in victory. Where, O death, is your victory?

Where, O death, is your sting?'"

1 Corinthians 15:51-55

Even if we live to be 101, it is nothing
compared to the eternity we will experience
in heaven with God after this life is long past.
Consider the words of One who defeated
death and came back to talk about it.

"And if I go and prepare a place for you,
I will come back and take you to be with
me that you also may be where I am."

John 14:3

This is not just an empty promise made
to gullible believers. Eleven of the twelve
disciples died a martyr's death, insisting they
had seen Jesus risen from the dead.

PUTTING IT ALL TOGETHER

"What is your life? You are a mist that appears for a little while and then vanishes."

James 4:14

Putting It All Together

Maybe after reading this book, you decide it's time to do a personal inventory of your life and examine how well you're doing constructing your "house" of longevity. Are you doing all that it takes to live out your potential? Remember, there are four pillars of longevity based on one strong foundation:

Section One
Pillar 1 - Have a Healthy Body: Take Care of Your House

Section Two
Pillar 2 - Focus on Blessing: Attitude Really Is Everything

Section Three
Pillar 3 - Love Somebody: You Are Made to Be with Others

Section Four
Pillar 4 - Stay Busy: The Surprising Secret to Longevity

Section Five
A Firm Foundation - Connecting with God

As you look at this list, which pillar needs a little bit of mortar? Which one do you need to be working on right now? The Holy Spirit will guide you because the answer is different for everyone. Over the next year, I want to challenge you to work diligently on whatever area you choose. Make those small changes, starting today.

The truth is that it doesn't matter how long you live on this earth—whether you live to be 10 or 110. The Bible says our lives are just a vapor and then they're gone (James 4:14). If we've lived the life God intended, the amazing spirit life starts after we die.

> "Just as man is destined to die once, and
> after that to face judgment, so Christ was
> sacrificed once to take away the sins of many
> people; and he will appear a second time, not
> to bear sin, but to bring salvation to those
> who are waiting for him."
> HEBREWS 9:27

All you have to do is accept His invitation and enter into a personal relationship with God through His Son, Jesus Christ. We're not talking about taking a class, or filling out a form or going online and passing a test. All you have to do is ask Christ into your life to begin a personal relationship with Him. Then put Him at the foundation of your life, and

He'll come in to live with you forever.

> "Here I am! I stand at the door and knock. If
> anyone hears my voice and opens the door,
> I will come in and eat with him, and he with
> me."

REVELATION 3:20

If you've never prayed a prayer to begin a
relationship with God through Christ, you might
pray something like this:

> *"God I need you. I've tried on my own, and I've*
> *failed. I'm not up to the task. I confess my sins, all*
> *of them—sins of omission, sins of commission. I've*
> *fallen short. I can't do it on my own. I can't live up*
> *to your standard of perfection.*
>
> *"Right now, Lord, I claim your forgiveness. Thank*
> *you for washing me clean and helping me start*
> *anew where I have failed in the past. I give you*
> *my life, all of it. It's in your hands. In Jesus' name,*
> *amen."*

Then get in a church where the Bible is taught.
Join in the fellowship! Enjoy living a LONG and
JOYFUL life!

Endnotes

Introduction

[1] Federal Interagency Forum on Aging-Related Statistics. *Older Americans 2012: Key Indicators of Well-Being.*

[2] Ibid.

[3] Dan Buettner, "The Island Where People Forget to Die," *New York Times*, October 25, 2012.

[4] Ibid.

[5] Michael E. McCullough, "Religious Involvement and Mortality: A Meta-Analytic Review," *Health Psychology*, Vol. 19, No. 3, 211-222.

[6] Ibid.

Pillar One

[7] Interview with Cal Sussman, *Esquire Magazine*, August 2004.

[8] Robert D. Smith, *20,000 Days and Counting*, Thomas Nelson, January 2013.

[9] Researchers at the National Center for Health Statistics in Maryland, part of the U.S. Centers for Disease Control and Prevention, conducted the study. Dr. Steven Heymsfield published an editorial response in the *Journal of the American Medical Association*, January 2, 2013.

[10] Scientists at the Pennington Biomedical Research Center conducted one such study, examining the

effects of alternate-day fasting on heart disease risk. After three weeks, the blood levels of triglycerides fell in men, but not in women. Women (but not men) also experienced increased "good," or HDL, cholesterol. Results published in the *American Journal Clinical Nutrition*, January 2005, vol. 81 no. 1 69-73.

[11] Dr. Dean Ornish, "Program For Reversing Heart Disease." Dr. Ornish's study of about 13,000 people revealed that people who walked 30 minutes daily (1.5 miles daily at 3 mph) are half as likely as unfit, sedentary people to die prematurely during the next eight years.

[12] A study of 11,000 residents around Atlanta, Georgia, revealed that people living in the suburbs walk less and weigh more than those living in the city. Each extra hour spent in a car relayed a 6% increased risk of obesity, according to an article in the June 2004 *American Journal of Preventive Medicine*.

[13] Interview with *That's Fit*, posted June 15, 2010.

[14] According to the Accreditation Council for Graduate Medical Education (ACGME).

Pillar Two

[15] According to *The British Journal of Sports Medicine*, October 2012, based on results from *Australian Diabetes, Obesity and Lifestyle Study*, an ongoing survey of the health habits of almost 12,000

Australian adults. By comparison, they concluded smoking a single cigarette reduces life expectancy by 11 minutes.

[16] Ibid. (for adults over 25)

[17] In 2012, Konstantinos Arfanakis, Ph.D., and colleagues from Rush University Medical Center and Illinois Institute of Technology in Chicago released information from their study of the positive effect of games, writing, reading and other mental activities on helping aging brains stay healthy. From a November 25, 2012, presentation to the Radiological Society of North America.

[18] According to research by Dr. Brian T. Gold, University of Kentucky, published in the *Journal of Neuroscience*, January 9, 2013.

Pillar Three

[19] Authored by A.A. Milne.

[20] The study was conducted by the Rochester Institute of Technology (RIT), overseen by Dr. Javier Espinosa. Researchers noted that men are adversely affected by the death of a spouse because they rely on their wives as their caregivers, physically and emotionally. RIT press release, October 19, 2012.

[21] Michael E. McCullough, "Religious Involvement and Mortality: A Meta-Analytic Review," *Health Psychology*, Vol. 19, No. 3, 211-222.

[22] Developmental psychologist Tiffany Field and her colleagues pioneered this study on premature babies

in the 1980s.

[23] Holt-Lunstad J, Smith TB, Layton JB (2010), "Social Relationships and Mortality Risk: A Meta-analytic Review," PLoS Med 7(7).

Pillar Four

[24] According to a study by Shell Health Services. Findings appeared in an online edition of the *British Medical Journal*.

[25] Andreas Kuhn, Jean-Philippe Wuellrich, Josef Zweimüller. *Fatal Attraction: Access to Early Retirement and Mortality*, March 2012. www.VoxEU. org accessed January 10, 2013.

[26] Howard S. Friedman, Leslie R. Martin, *The Longevity Project: Surprising Discoveries for Health and Long Life from the Landmark Eight-Decade Study*, Plume Publishing, March 2011 (e-book edition).

[27] Cal Newport, *So Good They Can't Ignore You: Why Skills Trump Passion in the Quest for Work You Love*, Business Plus, September 2012.

[28] Mary-Lou Weisman, "The History of Retirement from Early Man to A.A.R.P.," *The New York Times*, March 21, 1999.

[29] Mihaly Csikszentmihalyi, *Flow: The Psychology of Optimal Experience*, Harper Perennial Modern Classics, first edition July 2008.

A Firm Foundation—Connecting with God

[30] Billy Graham, Billy Graham's My Answer, Billy Graham Evangelistic Association www.billygraham.org, posted December 9, 2012.

Other Books by Charles R. Gordon:

In Plain Sight: Seeing God's Signature throughout Creation

Can you see what's hidden in plain sight? The similarities in the design of the universe are amazing. An oak tree looks like a brain cell. A hurricane shaped like a galaxy. A rose curled like a seashell. Is the connection just coincidence? Or is it something more?

Like an artist whose work is immediately recognizable, a Supreme Being has left his signature on all of creation for us to find. If you look closely, from microscopic algae to the largest nebula looming light years across in space, he has signed his name in repeated patterns and recognizable styles. But you have to look. So, open your eyes. Reawaken to wonder. And find yourself in awe of the mystery and greatness of God. This book features 40 devotions, each including a pairing of stunning color photos displaying striking similarities of design in God's creation.

Available at www.amazon.com

See more at www.DesignedOnPurpose.com